FLUTE PLAYALONG
TV Themes

WISE PUBLICATIONS
PART OF THE MUSIC SALES GROUP
LONDON / NEW YORK / PARIS / SYDNEY / COPENHAGEN / BERLIN / MADRID / HONG KONG / TOKYO

Published by

WISE PUBLICATIONS
14-15 Berners Street, London W1T 3LJ, UK

Exclusive Distributors:

MUSIC SALES LIMITED
Distribution Centre, Newmarket Road,
Bury St Edmunds, Suffolk IP33 3YB, UK

MUSIC SALES PTY LIMITED
20 Resolution Drive,
Caringbah, NSW 2229, Australia

Order No. AM1000296
ISBN 978-1-84938-502-2
This book © Copyright 2010 Wise Publications,
a division of Music Sales Limited.

Engraved by Camden Music.
New backing tracks by John Maul.
New arrangements by Chris Hussey.
Edited by Lizzie Moore.
CD recorded, mixed and mastered by Jonas Persson.
Cover designed & illustrated by Lizzie Barrand.

Printed in the EU

www.musicsales.com

YOUR GUARANTEE OF QUALITY
As publishers, we strive to produce every book
to the highest commercial standards.
The music has been freshly engraved and the book has
been carefully designed to minimise awkward page turns
and to make playing from it a real pleasure.
Particular care has been given to specifying acid-free,
neutral-sized paper made from pulps which have not been
elemental chlorine bleached. This pulp is from farmed
sustainable forests and was produced with special regard
for the environment.
Throughout, the printing and binding have been planned
to ensure a sturdy, attractive publication which should
give years of enjoyment.
If your copy fails to meet our high standards,
please inform us and we will gladly replace it.

Flute Fingering Chart

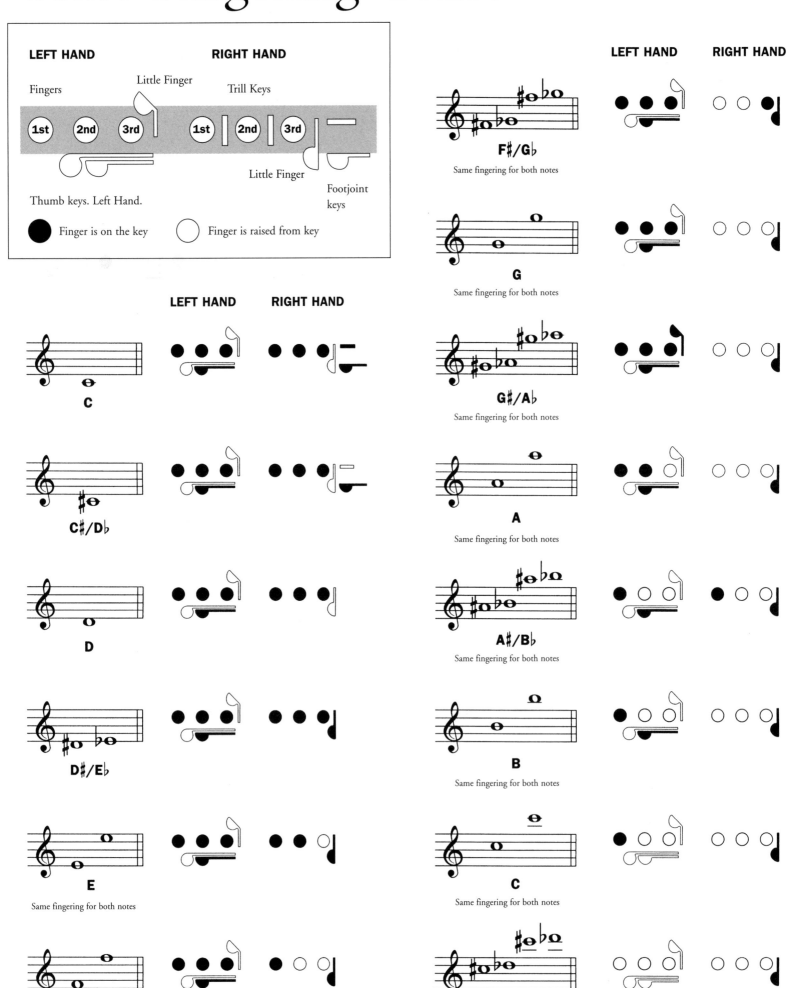

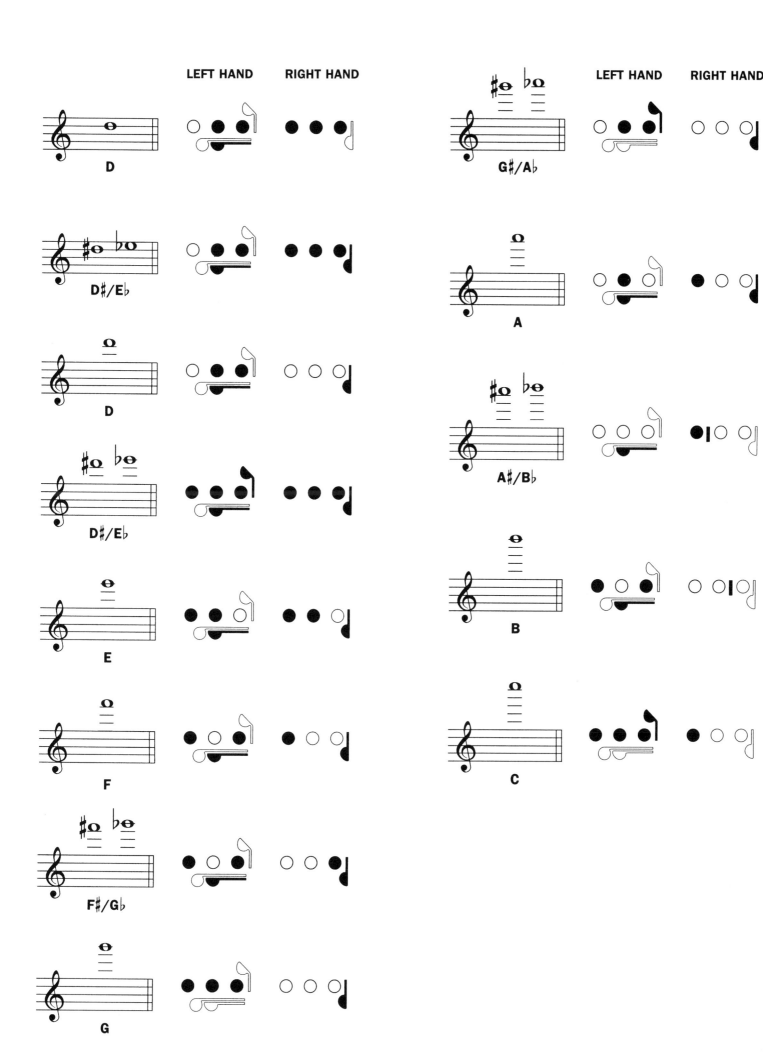

BLACKADDER

Music by Howard Goodall

BAND OF BROTHERS

Music by Michael Kamen

CAMPION

Music by Nigel Hess

With a lilt ♩ = 112

Mysteriously

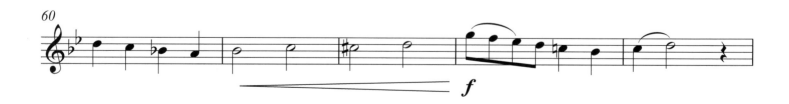

Confidently, with a swing

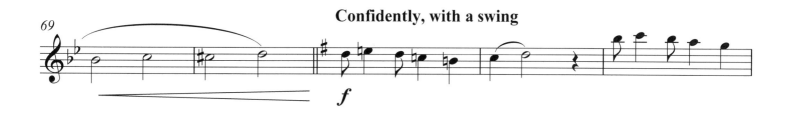

Slower

CHEERS ('WHERE EVERYBODY KNOWS YOUR NAME')

Words by Judy Hunt Angelo
Music by Gary Portnoy

rall.

FAWLTY TOWERS

Music by Dennis Wilson

EastEnders

Music by Simon May & Leslie Osborne

HOME AND AWAY

Words & Music by Mike Perjanik

to Coda ⊕

D.S. al Coda

⊕ Coda

rall.

Lovejoy

Music by Denis King

Miss Marple

Music by Ken Howard & Alan Blaikley

allargando e cresc.

Broadly, a tempo

molto rallentando

MISSION: IMPOSSIBLE

Music by Lalo Schifrin

Sex And The City

Music by Thomas Findlay, Andrew Cocup & Douglas Cuomo

THE OC ('CALIFORNIA')

Words & Music by Alex Greenwald, Jason Schwartzman, Al Jolson, Joseph Meyer, Buddy De Sylva, Darren Robinson, Jacques Brautbar & Sam Farrar

THE ODD COUPLE

Music by Neal Hefti

Steady and carefree (with a swing) ♩ = 116

1st time ***mf***, *2nd* ***f***

THE OFFICE ('HANDBAGS AND GLADRAGS')

Words & Music by Michael D'Abo

Agatha Christie's Poirot

Music by Christopher Gunning

PRIDE AND PREJUDICE

Music by Carl Davis

dolce

THE ROYLE FAMILY ('HALF THE WORLD AWAY')

Words & Music by Noel Gallagher

STAR TREK (TV THEME)

Music by Alexander Courage

Medium fast ♩ = 72

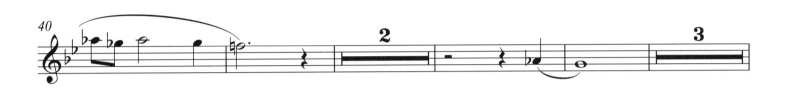

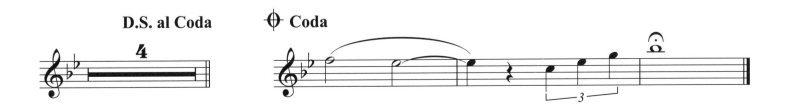

STRICTLY COME DANCING

Music by Daniel McGrath & Josh Phillips

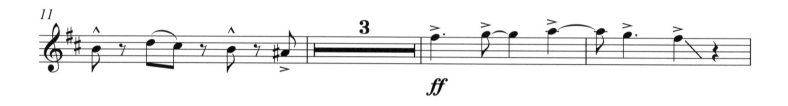

TAXI ('ANGELA')

Music by Bob James

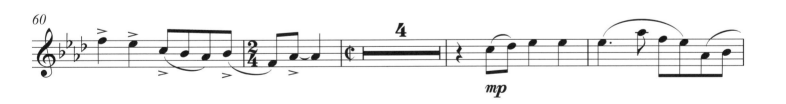

D.S. al Coda

⨁ **Coda**

123456789

CD Track Listing

Disc 1

Full performance tracks...

1. Blackadder
(Goodall) Noel Gay Music Company Limited

2. Band Of Brothers
(Kamen) Sony/ATV Music Publishing (UK) Limited/Warner/Chappell Music Limited

3. Campion
(Hess) Myra Music Limited

4. Cheers
(Angelo/Portnoy) Sony/ATV Harmony UK

5. Fawlty Towers
(Wilson) Dennis Wilson

6. EastEnders
(May/Osborne) Sony/ATV Music Publishing (UK) Limited

7. Home And Away
(Perjanik) Euston Music Limited

8. Lovejoy
(King) Witzend Music/Eaton Music Limited

9. Miss Marple
(Howard/Blaikley) Axle Music

10. Mission: Impossible
(Schifrin) Sony/ATV Music Publishing (UK) Limited

11. Sex And The City
(Findlay/Cocup/Cuomo) Warner/Chappell Music Limited/Copyright Control

12. The OC
(Greenwald/Schwartzman/Jolson/Meyer/Sylva/Robinson/Brautbar/Farrar)
Kobalt Music Publishing Limited/Redwood Music Limited/B. Feldman & Company

13. The Odd Couple
(Hefti) Sony/ATV Harmony (UK) Limited

14. The Office
(D'Abo) EMI United Partnership Limited

15. Poirot
(Gunning) Orchard Music Limited

16. Pride And Prejudice
(Davis) Faber Music Limited

17. The Royle Family
(Gallagher) Sony/ATV Music Publishing (UK) Limited

18. Star Trek
(Courage) Sony/ATV Music Publishing (UK) Limited

19. Strictly Come Dancing
(McGrath/Phillips) BBC Worldwide Music Limited

20. Taxi
(James) Sony/ATV Music Publishing (UK) Limited

Disc 2

Backing tracks only...

1. Blackadder

2. Band Of Brothers

3. Campion

4. Cheers

5. Fawlty Towers

6. EastEnders

7. Home And Away

8. Lovejoy

9. Miss Marple

10. Mission: Impossible

11. Sex And The City

12. The OC

13. The Odd Couple

14. The Office

15. Poirot

16. Pride And Prejudice

17. The Royle Family

18. Star Trek

19. Strictly Come Dancing

20. Taxi